MW00873214

A Family Walk

written by Jennifer Butenas

illustrated by Shennen Bersani

A Family Walk

Written by Jennifer Butenas

Illustrated by Shennen Bersani

Dad									
Mom		10		26	5	30			
Zac	9		8	23		5	37		
Ben		10	18		X	36			
Em♡			16	21	31				

There once was a time
after dinner was done,
when daytime had ended
and evening begun ...

The white linen curtain
blew in and about
on a comfortable breeze,
drawing everyone out.

It wasn't quite bedtime.
With two hours to spare,
the kids wished and hoped
Mom and Dad would be fair.

"Gonna shoot hoops!"
said Zac, ready to play.

"Catch?" wondered Ben,
in his easy-going way.

"Chalk," sang Emilee,
filled with delight.

"Late family walk!" said Mom,
lively and bright.

It was a *distinctively different,*
wishful and welcome
Moment in Time.

Outside the garage,
the leash hooked on Jazz,
birds singing, sun setting,
the sky a pizzazz ...

Zac thumped the basketball,
rhythmic and slow.
Ben had his ball and glove,
ready to throw.

Emilee wrote,
with an artistic plan,
her name on the driveway ...
and then took Mom's hand.

Past houses and lawns
all six made their way
on a neighborhood walk
at the end of the day.

It was a *rambling, roaming, struttin' and strollin'* **Moment in Time.**

Ben threw a pop-up
high in the sky.
Dad held his glove out
and focused his eye.

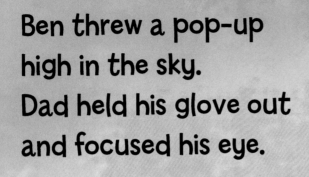

Dad caught the ball
and returned it to Ben.
Zac passed the basketball
... and then ...

Emilee shouted,
"Can't catch me!"
and ran to a landmark—
the great maple tree.

It was a *high-spirited,*
energetic and enthusiastic
Moment in Time.

The tree was majestic,
shading the road.
The kids liked to play there,
where stories were told.

The trunk was immense,
mighty and strong.
Its branches were plentiful,
graceful and long.

From summer to fall,
through winter and spring,
protective and watchful—
a neighborhood king!

It was a *ruggedly mighty,*
awe-inspiring
Moment in Time.

Jazz started sniffing
the base of the tree,
under branches, in holes,
exploring carefree.

Barking approval,
she sat down to see
Emilee climbing up
branch number three.

Ben found, much higher,
a branch strong and stable.
Zac, near the top,
was older and able.

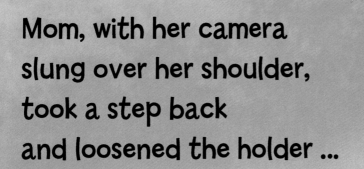

Mom, with her camera
slung over her shoulder,
took a step back
and loosened the holder ...

Lifted the camera,
aimed at the tree
and saw the whole family,
happy and free.

"Look over here!"
Mom called with a wave.
She pressed down and focused—
A moment to save!

Click! went the shutter.
It opened and closed,
and Mom caught a photo
while everyone posed.

Click!

It was a perfectly poised, momentous and memorable **Moment in Time.**

Mom snapped on the lens cap,
put camera in place
and said, "C'mon, monkeys!
We're off to home base."

Emilee swung on
a branch down low,
acting like a monkey
swinging to and fro.

Zac climbed down
from his perch up high
and threw Ben's baseball
way up in the sky.

Ben saw the ball and
jumped down from his seat,
caught the ball in his glove—
an outstanding feat!

Jazz led the way
as they walked down road,
heading back home
to their sweet abode.

It was a *playfully pleasant,* content and comfortable **Moment in Time.**

Now it was sunset.
The sun, a bright glow
out on the horizon,
was going down low.

The kids settled in.
Cool night came their way
as the sun carried with it
the warmth of the day.

The white linen curtain
blew in with the breeze,
quiet and graceful,
bringing comfort and ease.

Mom shut the window.
She didn't make a peep.
The white linen curtain
fell quiet with sleep.

Kids readied for bed
with soft, peaceful talk,
feeling cozy and loved
from their late family walk.

To every person, young and old, who sets aside
quality time to spend together as a family.
—Jen

To Heather Swiderski—mother, artist, friend.
—Shennen

A Family Walk
Copyright © Jennifer Butenas 2019
All rights reserved. No part of this book may be reproduced in any manner without the
written consent of the publisher except for brief excerpts in critical reviews or articles.

Written by Jennifer Butenas
Illustrated by Shennen Bersani
Book design by Jill Ronsley, suneditwrite.com

ISBN: 978-0-9840039-2-1 (softcover)
Library of Congress Control Number: 2018961367

Printed and bound in the USA

Published by The Perfect Moment, LLC
www.ThePerfectMomentllc.com
Stratham, New Hampshire 03885

The Perfect Moment, LLC